THE TRUTH THAT SETS US FREE

THE TRUTH THAT SETS US FREE

Biblical songs for worship

John L. Bell & Graham Maule
The Wild Goose Resource Group

WILD GOOSE PUBLICATIONS

First published in 2012
Reprinted 2013
© 2012 Wild Goose Resource Group, Iona Community, Glasgow G2 3DH, Scotland.
www.iona.org.uk/wgrg; www.wgrg.co.uk; www.holycity-glasgow.co.uk.

ISBN 978-1-84952-230-4

Published by Wild Goose Publications,
Fourth Floor, Savoy House, 140 Sauchiehall Street, Glasgow G2 3DH, UK,
the publishing division of the Iona Community.
Scottish Charity No. SC003794. Limited Company Reg. No. SC096243.
Web: www.ionabooks.com.

Distributed in Australia by Willow Connection Pty Ltd, Unit 4A, 3-9 Kenneth Road,
Manly Vale, NSW 2093, Australia, and in New Zealand by Pleroma Christian
Supplies, Higginson St., Otane 4170, Central Hawkes Bay, New Zealand.
Permission to reproduce any part of this work in Australia or New Zealand should be
sought from Willow Connection.

Design, layout and illustration by Graham Maule © 2012 Wild Goose Resource
Group, Iona Community, Glasgow G2 3DH, Scotland.

Music origination by Wild Goose Resource Group © 2012 Wild Goose Resource
Group, Iona Community, Glasgow G2 3DH, Scotland.

Printed by Bell & Bain, Glasgow, Scotland.

To D.M and C.M.,
generous and discerning friends
of our demanding common purpose.

Contents

Introduction

In an era when less and less may be assumed about the general public's knowledge of Jewish and Christian scripture, it is important that the Church does not forsake the deep pools of biblical truth for the shallows of saccharine personal piety.

This is particularly true of the song of the Church. Any analysis of 'popular' praise song collections will quickly identify a preponderance of the first person singular, 'I', even in texts intended to be sung by congregations for whom 'we' would be the more appropriate adjective.

One might also find a concentration on scriptural allusions which emphasise the need for praise at the expense of other expressions of devotion, and language about Jesus which precludes any suggestion that he might have caused embarrassment or offence.

This is not to say that such songs should be avoided, but rather that a congregation requires a balanced devotional diet which represents the full panoply of the magnificence of God and the experience of God's people.

In this collection, we have tried to offer, albeit in only 21 songs, a cross section of material for use in public worship. Most songs have biblical roots and references; some express exultant praise, others yearning or anger. Some are suited to one season or liturgical act, others are suitable for most Sundays.

Our hope is that they will add to the pool of similar material which takes both God and the world seriously, since it was for the world and not just humanity that Christ came.

John L. Bell
Graham Maule
June 2012

The songs in this collection have been recorded by the Wild Goose Collective on a CD of the same title.

The songs

Come with me

Hamba Nathi

Words & Music: South African traditional.

With vigour ♩ = 72

Ham - ba na - thi, ku - lu - lu we - thu._____
Come with me for the jour - ney is long._____

Ham - ba na - thi, ku - lu - lu we - thu._____
Come with me for the jour - ney is long._____

Ham - ba na - thi, ku - lu - lu we - thu._____
Come with me for the jour - ney is long._____

Words & Music South African traditional.

Hamba nathi, kululu wethu. (x4)
Kululu, kululu, kululu wethu. (x4)

Come with me for the journey is long. (x4)
The journey, the journey, the journey is long. (x2)

This South African song is very easy to learn and enjoyable to sing. Most parts only have three notes and it doesn't take long to learn them. The cantor may decide to improvise subsequent verses. All that is required is for other singers to hum the first two bars while s/he intones 'Pray with me' or 'Sing with me' ad lib. There are different rhythmic versions of this song, some starting on the upbeat, but this version can be easily sung by those who fear syncopation might ruin their health.

Light for our darkness

Words & Music: John L. Bell.

lift your wear - y   peo - ple from their   an - guish.____

lift   your   peo - ple from their   an - guish.____

Light for our darkness,
faith for disbelief,
health for mind and body when they languish;
Christ be among us, listen to our prayer,
lift your weary people from their anguish.

More of a choral introit or prayer chant than a congregational song, it is yet possible after a few hearings to have the assembly join in the song. It is best used during intercessory prayer or services of healing.

I cried aloud to God

Paraphrase (Ps.77, selected verses) & Arrangement: John L. Bell.
Melody: 'O KOU ALOHA NO', Queen Lili' Uokalami, 1895.

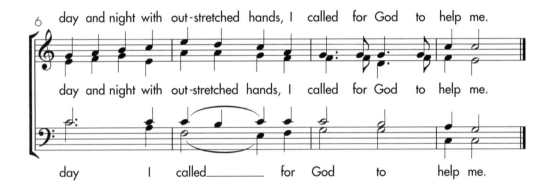

1.
I cried aloud to God
and God in kindness heard me;
by day and night with outstretched hands,
I called for God to help me.

1.
I cried aloud to God
and God___ heard me;
by day I called___
for God to help me.

2.
My tears ran ceaselessly,
I found no time for comfort;
and when I tried to think on God,
my fears would overwhelm me.

2.
My tears ran ceaselessly,
I found___ no comfort;
and when I tried___
my fears o'erwhelmed me.

3.
I feared that God had gone,
unwilling to show favour.
I wondered if indiff'rence had
replaced the Lord's compassion.

3.
I feared that God had gone,
to show favour.
I wondered what
replaced compassion.

4.
And then I brought to mind
how God is always faithful.
As in the past, so in these times,
the Lord will keep his promise.

4.
And then I brought to mind
how God is faithful.
As in the past___,
the Lord keeps promise.

5.
Then, I will praise the Lord
whose ears are ever open
to listen to each hurting soul:
God's grace will never fail me.

5.
Then, I will praise the Lord
whose ears are open
to listen, listen:
God, never fail me.

The U.S. State known as Hawai'i was originally an independent Pacific kingdom. At the end of the 19th century, the offspring of Protestant missionaries suggested to Washington that it was a land worth colonising. There ensued an invasion of the island, the disabling of what vestige there was of a police force, and the imprisonment of the queen.

While she was incarcerated, Queen Lili' Uokalami wrote the words and music of a lament which is still occasionally sung in Hawai'ian churches. It would be both insensitive and inappropriate for people who do not have Hawai'ian pedigree to sing the original text, but the sentiment of Psalm 77 is an appropriate substitute. This is a simple choral version.

So much wrong

Original words: Palestinian traditional.
Melody: 'AU SANG QU'UN DIEU', 16th C. French traditional.
Translation & Arrangement: John L. Bell.

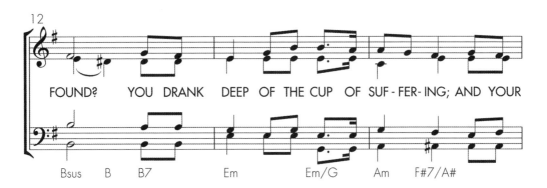

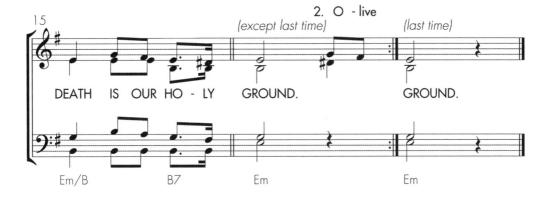

1.
So much wrong and so much injustice,
so you shouldered a wooden cross.
Now, like you, my best dreams are shattered;
all I know is the weight of loss.

Chorus:
MY BELOVED, MY BELOVED,
TELL ME WHERE CAN YOU BE FOUND?
YOU DRANK DEEP OF THE CUP OF SUFFERING,
AND YOUR DEATH IS OUR HOLY GROUND.

2.
Olive trees showed the pain of sorrow;
they were grieving for their Lord.
Round Jerusalem the hills were mourning
as the city denied its God.

3.
No fine song, no impressive music
can attempt to relieve my heart;
in this hour I am called to grieving,
lest no other will play this part.

4.
Everything I could ever offer
could not pay for what God has done;
but my life shall be spent in honour
of my Saviour, God's only Son.

We have relatively few songs from the Palestinian church, although it is one of the oldest in the world. However this text has come to us via a German collection of global songs. In it the singer speaks of devotion to and empathy for Jesus, his or her compatriot. The tune is not Middle Eastern in origin, but was probably transplanted there by missionaries or pilgrims to the Holy Land.

Save me, O God (Psalm 69)

Paraphrase (Psalm 69:1-6): John L. Bell.
Music: 'FLOOD', John L. Bell.

7 — C — Am7 — B

wa - ter has ris - en to my neck.
throat is_____ par - ched and sore.
more than the hairs up - on my head.
guilt is not hid - den from your sight.

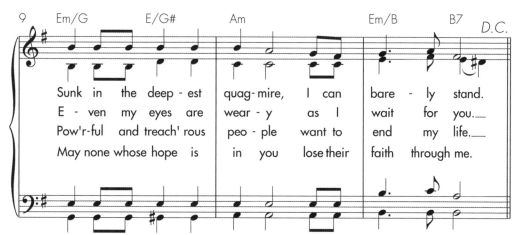

9 — Em/G — E/G# — Am — Em/B — B7 — D.C.

Sunk in the deep - est quag-mire, I can bare - ly stand.
E - ven my eyes are wear - y as I wait for you._____
Pow'r-ful and treach' rous peo - ple want to end my life._____
May none whose hope is in you lose their faith through me.

Antiphon:
SAVE ME! O GOD, HAVE MERCY
FOR THE FLOOD SWEEPS ME AWAY.

1.
Save me, O God, come quickly
For the water has risen to my neck.
Sunk in the deepest quagmire,
I can barely stand.

2.
I am worn out with weeping
and my throat is parched and sore.
Even my eyes are weary
as I wait for you.

3.
Those who, without cause, hate me
are more than the hairs upon my head.
Pow'rful and treach'rous people
want to end my life.

4.
God, well you know I'm foolish
and my guilt is not hidden from your sight.
May none whose hope is in you
lose their faith through me.

The psalms of doubt, despair and lament have a great but underestimated value. They offer a vocabulary for pain — physical, emotional, psychological and spiritual; and they allow people who suffer now to know that someone has been there before them, and that God has endorsed and heard their words. The antiphon in this setting is deliberately bleak; people who are depressed or discouraged seldom inhabit a wide vocal range.

Let my people go

Words & Melody: Traditional African American.
Arrangement: John L. Bell.

1.
When Israel was in Egypt's land,
    LET MY PEOPLE GO!
Oppressed so hard they could not stand,
    LET MY PEOPLE GO!

Refrain:
GO DOWN, MOSES
WAY DOWN IN EGYPT'S LAND,
TELL OLD PHARAOH,
TO LET MY PEOPLE GO.

2.
Thus saith the Lord, bold Moses said,
    LET MY PEOPLE GO!
If not I'll smite your first born dead,
    LET MY PEOPLE GO!

3.
No more in bondage shall they toil,
    LET MY PEOPLE GO!
Let them come out with Egypt's spoil,
    LET MY PEOPLE GO!

There is an abiding relevance in spirituals such as this. The ancient Hebrews cried out for release from the tyranny of the Egyptian Pharaoh. Centuries later, their story brought heart to enslaved African Americans in the southern states who cried out to be delivered from their bondage. Indeed this spiritual had a particular poignancy as it was sometimes sung to or about the Methodist Bishop Asbury, an abolitionist, urging him to confront the pharaohs of his day.

In our time, is there no slavery from which affluent westerners need released?

Alleluia (Greenbelt 10)

Words (adapted from Scripture): John L. Bell.
Music: 'GREENBELT 10', John L. Bell.

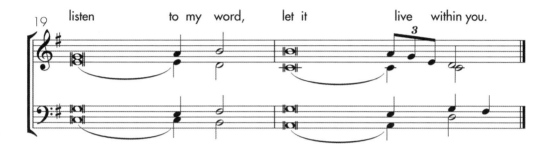

17 Today if you would hear my voice, harden not your hearts;

19 listen to my word, let it live within you.

ALLELUIA. (x8)

1.
To<u>day</u> if you would <u>hear</u> my <u>voice</u>,
<u>har</u>den <u>not</u> your <u>hearts</u>;
<u>lis</u>ten <u>to</u> my <u>word</u>,
<u>let</u> it <u>live</u> with<u>in</u> you.

2.
<u>All</u> I de<u>clare</u> to <u>you</u>
<u>I</u> have <u>heard</u> from the <u>Father</u>;
<u>this</u> I <u>gladly</u> <u>share</u>,
<u>let</u> your <u>ears</u> be <u>open</u>.

3.
<u>This</u> is the <u>Word</u> of the <u>Lord</u>,
<u>this</u> is the <u>Gospel</u> which <u>saves</u> us;
<u>this</u> is <u>food</u> for the <u>soul</u>,
<u>this</u> is <u>good</u> news for <u>ever</u>.

This is a gentle Alleluia which should be sung at a tempo and volume appropriate to the occasion. Though frequently used as a repetitive chant to accompany liturgical action, it may also be used with the verses sung by a cantor to greet the reading of the Gospel.

We worship Christ

Nzamuranza

Words & Melody: Xitswa 'Hallelujah' song, Mozambiquan traditional.
Translation: (chorus & verse 1) Patrick Matsikenyiri;
(verses 2-4); John L. Bell.
Arrangement: Patrick Matsikenyiri.

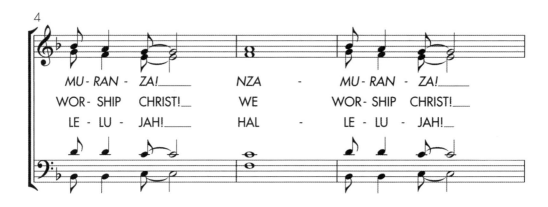

A -NGA - KO -   NA WA -KU -FA -NA -NA NA - YE,___
THERE IS   NO___ ONE WHO WILL   E -VER BE   LIKE___ HIM,___

Cantor:

a - nga - ko -   na wa -ku   fa -na -na Je - su.
there is   no___ one who will   e - ver be like___ him.

ALL: *D.C.*

A -NGA - KO - NA WA -KU -FA -NA -NA NA - YE.___
THERE IS   NO___ ONE WHO WILL   E -VER BE LIKE___ HIM.___

Chorus:
Cantor: Nzamuranza!
ALL: NZAMURANZA! NZAMURANZA!
            ANGAKONA WAKUFANANA NAYE.
Cantor: Nzamuranza!
ALL: NZAMURANZA! NZAMURANZA!
            ANGAKONA WAKUFANANA NAYE.

1a.

Cantor: Angakona wakufanana Jesu.
ALL: ANGAKONA WAKUFANANA NAYE.
Cantor: Angakona wakufanana Jesu.
ALL: ANGAKONA WAKUFANANA NAYE.

Chorus:
Cantor: We worship Christ!
ALL: WE WORSHIP CHRIST! WE WORSHIP CHRIST!
             THERE IS NO ONE WHO WILL EVER BE LIKE HIM.
Cantor: We worship Christ!
ALL: WE WORSHIP CHRIST! WE WORSHIP CHRIST!
             THERE IS NO ONE WHO WILL EVER BE LIKE HIM.

1b.

Cantor: There is no one who will ever be like him.
ALL: THERE IS NO ONE WHO WILL EVER BE LIKE HIM.
Cantor: There is no one who will ever be like him.
ALL: THERE IS NO ONE WHO WILL EVER BE LIKE HIM.

Chorus

2.

Cantor: There is no one who can teach like Jesus.
ALL: THERE IS NO ONE WHO WILL EVER BE LIKE HIM.
Cantor: There is no one who can preach like Jesus.
ALL: THERE IS NO ONE WHO WILL EVER BE LIKE HIM.

Chorus

3.

Cantor: There is no one who can sleep like Jesus.
ALL: THERE IS NO ONE WHO WILL EVER BE LIKE HIM.
Cantor: There is no one who can weep like Jesus.
ALL: THERE IS NO ONE WHO WILL EVER BE LIKE HIM.

Chorus

4.

Cantor: There is no one who can pray like Jesus.
ALL: THERE IS NO ONE WHO WILL EVER BE LIKE HIM.
Cantor: There is no one who will stay like Jesus.
ALL: THERE IS NO ONE WHO WILL EVER BE LIKE HIM.

Chorus (last time):
Cantor: Hallelujah!
ALL: HALLELUJAH! HALLELUJAH!
            THERE IS NO ONE WHO WILL EVER BE LIKE HIM.
Cantor: Hallelujah!
ALL: HALLELUJAH! HALLELUJAH!
            THERE IS NO ONE WHO WILL EVER BE LIKE HIM.

From Mozambique comes this magnificent acclamation. Though the indigenous language might seem awkward, it is actually very easy to sing. Children simply copy the sound their teacher makes; adults worry about the spelling and pronunciation.

The cantor may choose to sing either 'We worship Christ' or 'Hallelujah' after verses as appropriate.

The truth that sets us free

Words: John L. Bell.
Music: 'ESKE', John L. Bell.

Moderato ♩ = 72

When the wheel of fate is turn - ing and the mills of God grind slow; when the past seems more at - tract - ive than the fu - ture we don't know; when our

(Hum)

con - fi - dence is wa - ning and we lack se - cur - i -

ty, comes the time - less word of Je - sus that the

(text)

truth will set us free.

1.
When the wheel of fate is turning
and the mills of God grind slow;
when the past seems more attractive
than the future we don't know;
when our confidence is waning
and we lack security,
comes the timeless word of Jesus
that the truth will set us free.

2.
Is it war or economics,
is it danger or deceit,
is it unforeseen depression,
fear of failure to compete?
Have the times which once were changing
led where no one wants to be?
Shall we live by lies on offer
or the truth that sets us free?

3.
With real faith there will be doubting,
and with loss there will be grief;
no one knows the contradictions
which will exercise belief.
Against conflicts life might bring us
God provides no guarantee,
just this word of hope and healing:
know that truth will set you free.

4.
So, dear Jesus, make us willing
to unmask convenient lies,
to protest wherever power
closes conscience, ears and eyes;
and release our expectations
of your kingdom, yet to be,
born in courage, joy and justice
and the truth that sets us free.

One of the memorable truths which Jesus articulates in John's Gospel is that 'You shall know the truth and the truth shall set you free.' In many areas of life these words need to be affirmed, whether that has to do with our personal health or what enables or disables the security of the world.

Come and find rest in Christ

Words: Swee Hong Lim (amended).
Melody: '宝贵／Bao Gui', Swee Hong Lim.
Arrangement: John L. Bell.

Come and find rest in Christ,___

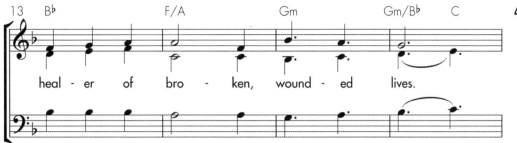

heal - er of bro - ken, wound - ed lives.

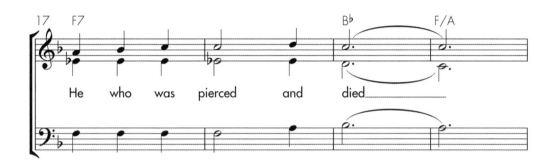

He who was pierced and died_____

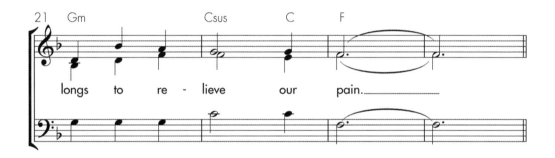

longs to re - lieve our pain._____

Interlude

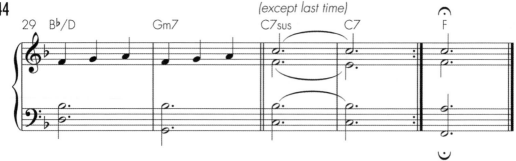

1.
Come and find rest in Christ,
healer of broken, wounded lives.
He who was pierced and died
longs to relieve our pain.

2.
Where can we run and hide,
shamed and rejected if we be?
Where Jesus' spirit breathes
all are made whole through love.

3.
Jesus throws wide the net,
gathers the broken, finds the lost.
Come and be nursed by God;
trust in his care and live.

Swee Hong Lim is a Singaporean Chinese Methodist who is now a professor at Emmanuel College in Toronto. He has a beautiful feel for singable melody and engaging text, as is evident in this song for healing.

Peace I leave

Paraphrase (John 14:17) & Music: John L. Bell.

Peace I leave, my peace I give you,
not the peace the world can offer.
In each storm, in each confusion
I'll be with you.

Theses are words from the Gospel, and our experience has been that when people sing texts such as this in church they frequently recall the words and tune to mind as part of their personal devotions. The chant may be used at a service of reconciliation or during the reception of Holy Communion.

Fellow travellers

Words: John L. Bell.
Music: 'FELLOW TRAVELLERS', John L. Bell.

With curiosity ♩ = 60

Is God, who made and

loves the earth,___ who gave each self and each

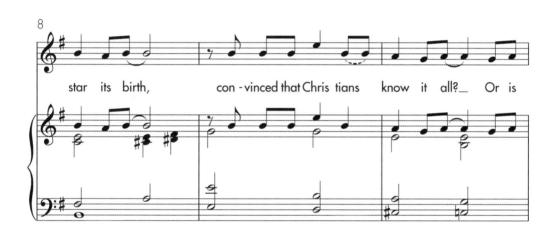

star its birth, con-vinced that Chris tians know it all?___ Or is

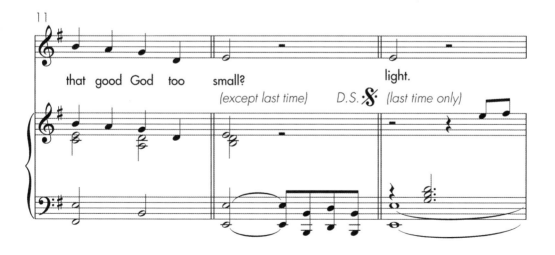

that good God too small?

(except last time) D.S. 𝄋 *(last time only)*

light.

1.
Is God, who made and loves the earth,
who gave each self and each star its birth,
convinced that Christians know it all?
Or is that good God too small?

2.
Did Jesus Christ, the faithful Jew,
claim God was patron of just a few
content to keep with a chosen race
and to limit heaven's embrace?

3.
Did he not show immense respect
for followers of a less favoured sect,
delighted when the faith shone clear
in the faithful others fear?

4.
Do we presume the Muslim mind
what Buddhists claim or what Hindus find
is purely human in design,
quite detached from the Divine?

5.
God, bless the faith we call our own,
each word we cherish, each seed you've sown.
Yet humble us till all believe
you are more than we conceive.

6.
Encourage us to look and care
for gifts you've given which others share,
all those who walk by faith, not sight,
fellow travellers led by light.

The presumption that Jesus only mixed with Jews and the occasional Samaritan is hit on the head with the Gospel witness that he amicably related to at least six ethnicities other than his own. Recently Indian theologians have suggested that because of the trade routes from the Far to the Middle East, it is possible that Jesus could have been aware of Hindu and Buddhist traditions.

Perhaps this and his reluctance to condemn those who were 'different' are important facts for Christians to accept when speaking of, or living in, multi-cultural societies.

Malembe

Original Words & Music: Joseph Kabemba Mwenze.
Translation: Carolyn Kappauf.

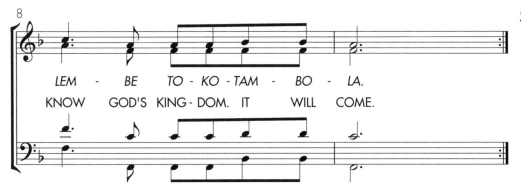

LEM - BE TO - KO -TAM - BO - LA.
KNOW GOD'S KING - DOM. IT WILL COME.

1a. *Cantor:* *Na nzela na lola tokotambola malembe,*
    ALL: MALEMBE TOKOTAMBOLA.
    (Repeat)

    Refrain: MALEMBE, MALEMBE,
    MALEMBE TOKOTAMBOLA.
    (Repeat)

1b. *Cantor:* As long as we live, there is a future for creation,
    ALL: A FUTURE FOR THE UNIVERSE.
    (Repeat)

    Refrain: WE KNOW THIS, WE KNOW THIS,
    WE KNOW GOD'S KINGDOM. IT WILL COME.
    (Repeat)

2. *Cantor:* As long as we sing, there is a future for creation,
   ALL: A FUTURE FOR THE UNIVERSE.
   (Repeat)

3. *Cantor:* As long as we pray, there is a future for creation,
   ALL: A FUTURE FOR THE UNIVERSE.
   (Repeat)

4. *Cantor:* As long as we move, there is a future for creation,
   ALL: A FUTURE FOR THE UNIVERSE.
   (Repeat)

An easy way to learn this song is to have a soloist sing each half and then have it repeated by the Assembly. The cantor can freely improvise verses simply by changing one word.

We shall break bread

Words: John L. Bell.
Music: 'FRACTIO' John L. Bell.

1.
We shall break bread as Jesus did before us
in fields and banquets, in an upstairs room.
His true companions meet around a table:
we shall break bread.

2.
We shall break bread because the world is hungry,
and Jesus showed us how to love and care.
All life is gift; each gift is meant for sharing:
we shall break bread.

3.
We shall break bread and thus we will remember
how he was broken that we might be whole.
His life laid down shall raise us up forever:
we shall break bread.

4.
We shall break bread and in this celebration
be one with friends who sit at heaven's great feast.
They see the host whose presence is among us:
we shall break bread.

5.
Here in the bread and wine which earth supplies us
refined by skill and will of human hands,
we taste the depth and richness of God's goodness:
we shall break bread.

6.
Glory to God whose providence sustains us,
glory to Christ who calls us to his feast;
and to the Spirit, source of transformation:
let us break bread,
let us break bread.

The celebration of the eucharist has multiple resonances. It is not simply a memorial feast, it is also a foretaste of heaven, a continuation of the table meals of which Jesus was fond, and many things beside. This unison song is therefore best suited to be sung before or during the receiving of Holy Communion.

How could a crowd?

Words: John L. Bell.
Music: 'CHANNELS OF MERCY', John L. Bell.

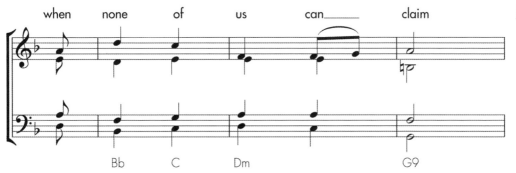

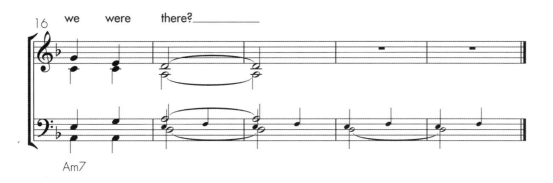

1.
How could a crowd with no sign of provisions
dine in a desert and leave some food to spare?
How can our minds understand or believe it
when none of us can claim we were there?

2.
How can a world with excess of provisions
sidestep the hungry and hesitate to care?
How can the wealthy engage in denial
when all know here what crowds suffer there?

3.
Still we exhibit selective indifference,
talking statistics and charting the need;
privileged spectators, we rail at injustice
and question God but pamper our greed…

4.
Had we been there when a boy, without prompting,
put loaves and fishes into Jesus' hands,
we might have seen how unselfish compassion
works miracles a child understands.

5.
Jesus, who showed how both justice and mercy
are prime ingredients in God's daily bread,
bless and disturb us to forfeit advantage
till all are privileged, valued and fed.

The miracle of the feeding of the five thousand is perhaps *the* miracle needing to be taken most seriously by Christians if the world is to survive. Essentially the story is about Jesus taking on human selfishness and transforming it into generosity. Then there was enough food for the crowd; now there is enough food for the world. It is the channels of distribution which are in sore need of redemption.

The first three lines of text may be sung in 2-part harmony, the last in 4-parts.

Jikelele

Original Words & Melody: Zulu traditional, South African,
(transcribed by Maggie Hamilton).
Translation & Arrangement: Zulu traditional, South African.

Refrain:
JIKELELE. (x8)

1.
Jikelele. (x4)

2a.
uJesu ngiyama zi uhamb'izwe lonke, jikelele, jikelele.

2b.
We'll walk with Jesus around the world.

Here is an amazingly simple and effective Zulu song from South Africa. Everyone who sings the chorus has only four notes and four syllables to remember. 'Jikelele' essentially expresses that God is everywhere, universal. The chorus should establish itself by singing the four bar sequence twice, then the cantor sings a verse, and the process repeats for verse two, closing with the chorus sung ad lib.

Soft falls the snow

Words: John L. Bell.
Music: 'WINTER'S WORSHIP', John L. Bell.

Tenderly ♩ = 84

Soft falls the snow, soon comes the win- try weath - er when cold is

cruel or kind, and days are dark, in which some

see rare beau - ty be - yond meas - ure, while oth - ers

fear where fate will leave its mark, while oth - ers

fear   where   fate   will leave   its   mark._____

1.
Soft falls the snow,
soon comes the wintry weather
when cold is cruel or kind, and days are dark,
in which some see rare beauty beyond measure,
while others fear where fate will leave its mark,
while others fear where fate will leave its mark.

2.
Soft falls the snow,
and streets, surprised by silence,
witness the primal power of mother earth
as winter offers worship to its Maker,
who sowed the snow and brought the rain to birth,
who sowed the snow and brought the rain to birth.

3.
Soft falls the snow,
but will it fall forever
if we mistreat the world we do not own?
If nature knelt, condemned to be our servant,
who can foresee what dread would then be known?
Who can foresee what dread would then be known?

4.
Soft falls the snow.
Send with it, Lord, your blessing
to help us love the earth as is your will,
grateful for different gifts in different seasons –
the light, the dark, the vibrant and the still,
the light, the dark, the vibrant and the still.

The relationship mandated in the Bible between humanity and the physical world is very
straightforward. We are to be guardians and servants of the soil. Most hymns about nature
celebrate its beauty, but in the present environmental predicament, it is important that we
preserve as often and as much as we admire.

Blessing and honour (2012)

Words: John L. Bell.
Music: 'COLOSSIANS', John L. Bell.

Vigorously ♩ = 72

BLESS-ING AND HO-NOUR, GLO-RY AND POWER.

WOR-SHIP AND WIS-DOM, HIGH THANKS-GIV - ING:

THESE ALL BE-LONG TO GOD AND THE LAMB;

13 WOR-THY ARE THEY OF PRAISE EV - ER - MORE.

17 Ho - ly is God,__ sov' - reign of all,

(Hum)

21 God who gave birth to cre - a - tion;

25 God who in Je - sus, flesh of our flesh,

D.C.

re - con - ciles   all,   re - con - ciles   all.

BLESSING AND HONOUR,
GLORY AND POWER,
WORSHIP AND WISDOM
HIGH THANKSGIVING:
THESE ALL BELONG
TO GOD AND THE LAMB;
WORTHY ARE THEY
OF PRAISE EVERMORE.

1.
Holy is God, sov'reign of all,
God who gave birth to creation;
God who in Jesus, flesh of our flesh,
reconciles all, reconciles all.

2.
Neighbour and stranger, welfare and wealth,
diff'rence in age, faith or nation —
opposites can be made one. In Christ
all things connect, all things connect.

3.
How to turn enemies into close friends,
and preserve this precious planet;
how we should live so all can survive —
this is Christ's cause; these are God's laws.

4.
Banker and claimant, pauper and prince,
lawyers and justice campaigners,
left wing and right wing and all between —
none is left out. Therefore we shout,

The antiphon or chorus of this song comes from the book of Revelation 5:13, but the text gathers round the ancient hymn or credal statement in Colossians 1:13-20, that all things are reconciled, held together in Christ.

I love the Lord (Psalm 116)

Paraphrase (Ps.116:1-4, 8-9 & 13-14): John L. Bell.
Music: 'NEW FENWICK', John L. Bell.

1.
I love the Lord because he heard
my deep and earnest prayer;
all that I hold within my heart
God listens to,
God listens to with care.

2.
I felt ensnared by chains of death,
hell had me in its grasp;
distress, anxiety and fear
were all my hands,
were all my hands could clasp.

3.
And then I cried out to the Lord,
'O God, deliver me.'
To God, the merciful, I cried,
whose faithful love,
whose faithful love sets free.

4.
The Lord delivered me from death
and dried my eyes of tears;
God kept my feet from losing grip
and quietened,
and quietened all my fears.

5.
What shall I offer to the Lord
for all the good that came?
I'll lift salvation's holy cup
and gladly bless,
and gladly bless God's name.

The only direct allusion we have to Jesus singing happens after he has instituted what we now call the Sacrament of Holy Communion. Before leaving for Gethsemane, he and the disciples sang a hymn. This refers to the second part of the Hallel psalms (Psalms 115-118). So, in a very real way, when we sing this psalm we do it in solidarity with Jesus.

Jeye ho

Text: Indian, author unknown; amended by John L. Bell.
Melody: 'JEYE HO', Indian traditional, arranged by John L. Bell.

HO,⏤ JE-YE, JE-YE, JE-YE, JE-YE, HO. JE-YE

JE-YE HO, JE-YE

Chorus: *JEYE HO A HO, (x4)*
 JEYE, JEYE, JEYE, JEYE HO, (x2)

1. You are the one deserving our rev'rence,
    JE, JEYE HO,
 therefore we bow in your divine presence.
    JE, JEYE HO,
 Humble our worship, gracious your greeting,
 gladly we praise you, ever repeating:
    JEYE, JEYE, JEYE, JEYE HO, (x2)

Chorus

2. Pardon our sins and grant us a vision,
    JE, JEYE HO,
 show us on earth the pathway to heaven.
    JE, JEYE HO,
 Keep us together under your protection
 so that, as one, we move in your direction.
    JEYE, JEYE, JEYE, JEYE HO, (x2)

Chorus

This wonderful Hindi hymn has a chorus easily sung in parts by congregations. The men gradually build up a mantra, a fifth and a ninth above the tonic, the women sing the tune, and all sing the last four bars in unison. For a more authentic experience, the verses may be added. The Hindi refrain is essentially an acclamation of God's greatness.

'*Jeye ho*' may loosely be translated as 'Glory be to God'.

Alleluia, praise the Lord

Aleluya Y'in Oluwa

*Words & Music: Nigerian, author unknown,
(as taught by Emmanuel Badejo, Nigeria).*

Joyfully ♩ = 60

1a. A - le - lu - ya, Y'in O - lu - wa. A - le - lu - ya,
1b. Al - le - lu - ia, praise the Lord.___ Al - le - lu - ia,
2. Songs of joy sing to the Lord.___ Songs of joy sing
3. Beat the drums and wor - ship God.___ Beat the drums and

Y'in O - lu - wa. O seun, o seun, o seun,
praise the Lord.___ Prais - es, high prais - es, now
to the Lord.___ Danc - ing and sing - ing your
wor - ship God.___ Prais - es, high prais - es, give

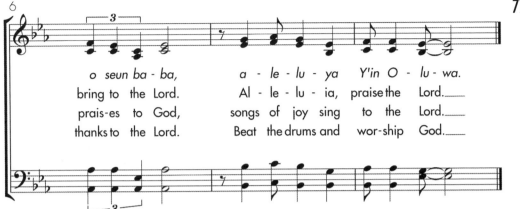

1a.
Aleluya, Y'in Oluwa.
Aleluya, Y'in Oluwa.
O seun, o seun, o seun, o seun baba,
aleluya Y'in Oluwa.

1b.
Alleluia, praise the Lord.
Alleluia, praise the Lord.
Praises, high praises, now bring to the Lord,
alleluia, praise the Lord.

2.
Songs of joy sing to the Lord.
Songs of joy sing to the Lord.
Dancing and singing your praises to God,
songs of joy sing to the Lord.

3.
Beat the drums and worship God.
Beat the drums and worship God.
Praises, high praises, give thanks to the Lord,
beat the drums and worship God.

From Nigeria comes this lively Alleluia, the first verse of which can either be sung in English or the indigenous language. It can be both a call to and a response to worship, and is best sung *a capella* with a drum accompaniment.

Alphabetical index of first lines

The Iona Community

The Iona Community is:
- an ecumenical movement of men and women from different walks of life and different traditions in the Christian church;
- committed to the gospel of Jesus Christ, and to following where that leads, even into the unknown;
- engaged together, and with people of goodwill across the world, in acting, reflecting and praying for justice, peace and the integrity of creation;
- convinced that the inclusive community we seek must be embodied in the community we practise.

Together with our staff, we are responsible for:
- our islands residential centres of Iona Abbey, the MacLeod Centre on Iona, and Camas Adventure Centre on the Ross of Mull;
- and in Glasgow: the administration of the Community,
- our work with young people;
- our publishing house, Wild Goose Publications;
- our association in the revitalising of worship with the Wild Goose Resource Group.

The Iona Community was founded in Glasgow in 1938 by George MacLeod, minister, visionary and prophetic witness for peace, in the context of the poverty and despair of the Depression. Its original task of rebuilding the monastic ruins of Iona Abbey became a sign of hopeful rebuilding of community in Scotland and beyond. Today, we are about 270 members, mostly in Britain, and about 1500 associate members, with over a thousand friends worldwide. Together and apart, 'we follow the light we have, and pray for more light'.

For information on the Iona Community contact:
The Iona Community, 4th Floor, Savoy House,
140 Sauchiehall Street, Glasgow G2 3DH, UK
Tel: **+44 (0)141 332 6343**
E-mail: **admin@iona.org.uk**
Web: **www.iona.org.uk**

For enquiries about visiting Iona, please contact:
Iona Abbey, Isle of Iona, Argyll PA76 65N, UK
Tel: **+44 (0)1681 700404**
E-mail: **ionacomm@iona.org.uk**

Wild Goose Publications

The publishing house of the Iona Community, established in the Celtic Christian tradition of Saint Columba, produces books, CDs and digital downloads on:
- holistic spirituality
- social justice
- political and peace issues
- healing
- innovative approaches to worship
- songs for worship, including the work of the Wild Goose Resource Group
- material for meditation and reflection

For more information, please contact us at:
Wild Goose Publications,
Iona Community, 4th Floor, Savoy House,
140 Sauchiehall Street, Glasgow G2 3DH, Scotland.

Tel: **+44 (0)141 332 6292;** Fax: **+44 (0)141 332 1090**
E-mail: **admin@ionabooks.com**

Web: **www.ionabooks.com** (details of products and online sales).

The Wild Goose Resource Group

The Wild Goose Resource Group is an expression of the Iona Community's commitment to the renewal of public worship. Based in Glasgow, the WGRG has three resource workers, John Bell, Jo Love and Graham Maule, who lead workshops, seminars and events throughout Britain and abroad. They are supported by Gail Ullrich, who fulfils the role of the Group's administrator.

The task of the WGRG has been to develop and identify new methods and materials to enable the revitalisation of congregational song, prayer and liturgy. Songs and liturgical material have been translated and used in many countries across the world as well as being frequently broadcast on radio and television. All music in this collection has been recorded by the Wild Goose Collective — an ad hoc assortment of singers associated with the Resource Group.

The WGRG, along with a committed group of fellow-Glaswegians, run *Holy City*, a monthly ecumenical workshop and worship event for adults in the centre of Glasgow.

The WGRG also publish a mail-order catalogue, an annual *Liturgy Booklet* series and a twice-yearly newsletter, *GOOSEgander*, to enable friends and supporters to keep abreast of WGRG developments.

If you would like to find out more about subscribing to these, or about ways to support the WGRG financially, please contact:

Wild Goose Resource Group,
Iona Community, 4th Floor, Savoy House,
140 Sauchiehall Street, Glasgow G2 3DH, Scotland.

Tel: **0141 332 6343;** Fax: **0141 332 1090**
E-mail: **wgrg@iona.org.uk**

Web: **www.iona.org.uk/wgrg** (for information)
       www.wgrg.co.uk (for online sales)
       www.holycity-glasgow.co.uk

Twitter: **'WildGooseRG'** and **'HolyCityGlasgow'**
Facebook: **'Wild Goose Resource Group'** and **'Holy City Glasgow'**

We Walk His Way: Short songs for worship, Vol.3, John L. Bell & Wild Goose Collective

The third in the series of wee songs that have proved to be hugely popular and useful in English-speaking countries and several of the songs have been translated into other European languages. Some shorter songs bear continual repetition for meditation or as an accompaniment to liturgical action; some may be interspersed with prayer or scripture reading, some – like the Sanctus – have a particular place in the celebration of Holy Communion. But all, being short, are memorable. They can link us to the greater universal church; they may provide for our memory words which are worth keeping; and they may be the means whereby people who have never sung in harmony get a foot up that ladder. Book: ISBN 9781905010554; CD: ISBN 9781905010424

I Will Not Sing Alone: Songs for the seasons of love, John L. Bell & Wild Goose Collective

A deliberately eclectic collection of words & music from different ages, fused in contemporary arrangements. The seventeen songs include exclamations of praise, meditative reflections on the love of God, laments for the loss of a child and for countries at war. Book: 9781901557916; CD: ISBN 9781901557893

10 Things They Never Told Me About Jesus: A beginner's guide to a larger Christ, John L. Bell

Not another book about what we already know, but one about what we overlook. Here, John Bell explores facets of the personal life, relationships and ministry of Jesus which are seldom the stuff of preaching or conversation, but which are all rooted in the Gospels and are necessary if we are to be freed from the passive stereotypes which still dominate thinking about Christ. Book: ISBN 9781905010608

The Singing Thing: A case for congregational song, John L. Bell

One of the world's experts on congregational song writes for those who want to encourage others to sing or sing better. He offers ten persuasive answers to the question 'Why do we sing?' Each answer is explored with a wealth of practical insight born of the author's twenty years of experience in this field. Book: ISBN 9781901557282

The Singing Thing Too: Enabling congregations to sing, John L. Bell

The second of John Bell's books dealing with the case for congregational song. Here he deals with the 'how to' issues, the techniques of teaching songs to congregations and groups. Describing this process as 'an exercise in communicating truth through personality', drawing on both his own and colleagues' extensive and devoted practical experience, John crystallises the distinctive WGRG approach which has inspired and enthused countless folk to sing, often despite their own misgivings, over the last 25

years. A crucial resource for those interested in helping God's people find their voices.
Book: ISBN 9781905010325

SONGBOOKS/ OCTAVO PACKS/ CDs

Come All You People (Book/CD), John L. Bell; ISBN 9780947988685/ 9781901557404

Courage To Say No (Book/CD), John L. Bell & Graham Maule; ISBN 9780947988784/ 9781901557442

Enemy Of Apathy (Book), John L. Bell & Graham Maule; ISBN 9780947988272

God Comes Tomorrow (Octavo Pack/CD) John L. Bell; GIA G-4376/ GIA CD-494

God Never Sleeps (Octavo Pack/CD) John L. Bell; GIA G-4376/ GIA CD-348

Heaven Shall Not Wait (Bk/CD), John L. Bell & Graham Maule; ISBN 9781901557800/ 9781901557459

Innkeepers & Light Sleepers (Book/CD), John L. Bell; ISBN 9780947988470/ 9781901557398

Last Journey, The (Book/Octavo Pack/CD), John L. Bell; GIA G-4527P/ GIA G-4527/ GIA CD-381

Love & Anger (Book/ CD), John L. Bell & Graham Maule; ISBN 9780947988982/ 9781901557411

Love From Below (Book/ CD), John L. Bell & Graham Maule; ISBN 0 947988 34 3/ 9781901557466

One Is The Body (Book/ CD), John L. Bell; ISBN 9781901557350/ 9781901557374

Psalms Of Patience, Protest & Praise (Book/ CD), John L. Bell; ISBN 9780947988562/ 9780947988579

Seven Psalms Of David (Octavo Pack), John L. Bell; GIA G-4830

Seven Songs Of Mary (Book), John L. Bell; GIA G-4652

Seven Songs Of Mary & Seven Psalms of David (CD), John L. Bell; GIA CD-403

Splendour Of The House Of God, The (Octavo Pack/ CD), John L. Bell; GIA G-8099; GIA CD-874

There Is One Among Us (Book/ CD), John L. Bell; ISBN 9781901557107/ 9781901557213

Take This Moment (Octavo Pack/ CD), John L. Bell; GIA G-5155 / GIA CD-464

When Grief is Raw (Book), John L. Bell & Graham Maule; ISBN 9780947988913

Cloth for the Cradle (Book), Wild Goose Worship Group; ISBN 9781901557015

He Was In The World (Book), John L Bell; ISBN 9780947988708

Jesus & Peter (Book), John L. Bell & Graham Maule; ISBN 9781901557176

Present On Earth (Book), Wild Goose Worship Group; ISBN 9781901557640

Stages On The Way (Book), Wild Goose Worship Group; ISBN 9781901557114

Wee Worship Book, A (Book), John L. Bell & Mairi Munro; ISBN 9781901557190

REFLECTIONS

All That Matters: collected scripts from Radio 4's Thought for The Day, Vol.2 (Book), John L. Bell; ISBN 9781849520706

Hard Words For Interesting Times: Biblical texts in contemporary contexts (Book), John L. Bell   ISBN 9781901557756

States Of Bliss & Yearning: the marks and means of authentic Christian spirituality (Book), John L. Bell; ISBN 9781901557077

Thinking Out Loud; collected scripts from Radio 4's Thought for The Day, Vol.1 (Book), John L. Bell; ISBN 9781905010417

WGRG LITURGY BOOKLETS

God & Her Girls: a celebration of the giftedness of forgotten women - Liturgy Booklet no.11; Wild Goose Resource Group; WGRG 011

Harvesting The World: a liturgy for havest festivals - Liturgy Booklet no.10; Wild Goose Resource Group; WGRG 010

A Family Affair: a liturgy based on Jesus' most famous parable (the Prodigal Son) - Liturgy Booklet no.9; Wild Goose Resource Group; WGRG 009

Fencing In God's People: a liturgy on 3000 years of wall building in Israel & Palestine - Liturgy Booklet no.8; Wild Goose Resource Group; WGRG 008

A Road To Roam: a way of celebrating sacred space - Liturgy Booklet no.7; Wild Goose Resource Group; WGRG 007

Sweet Honey & Hard Places: prayer services based on the Psalms - Liturgy Booklet no.6; Wild Goose Resource Group; WGRG 006

Pictures Of God: an act of worship about images - Liturgy Booklet no.5; Wild Goose Resource Group; WGRG 005

Remember Me Today: a Holy Week reflection - Liturgy Booklet no.4; Wild Goose Resource Group; WGRG 004

The Love Which Heals: a service of grieving & gratitude for those recently bereft - Liturgy Booklet no.3; Wild Goose Resource Group; WGRG 003

A Jubilee Liturgy: - Liturgy Booklet no.2; Wild Goose Resource Group; WGRG 002

St Columba Of Iona: An order for the commemoration of the saint's life - Liturgy Booklet no.1; Wild Goose Resource Group; WGRG 001

Order online at www.ionabooks.com or www.wgrg.co.uk